The Little Book of Pollinators

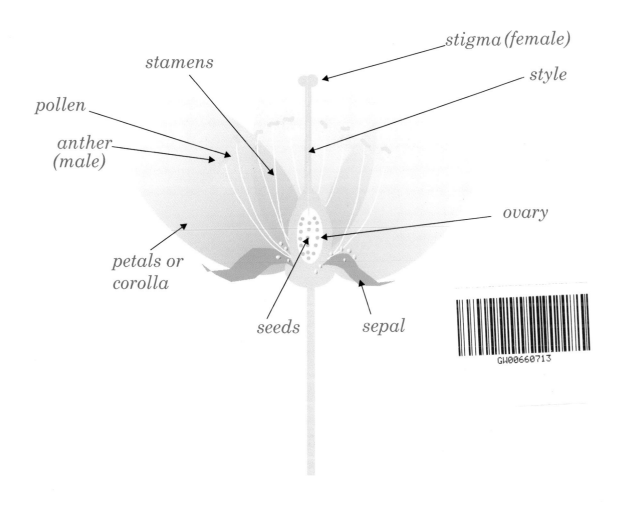

stigma (female)

style

stamens

pollen

anther
(male)

ovary

petals or
corolla

seeds

sepal

GW00660713

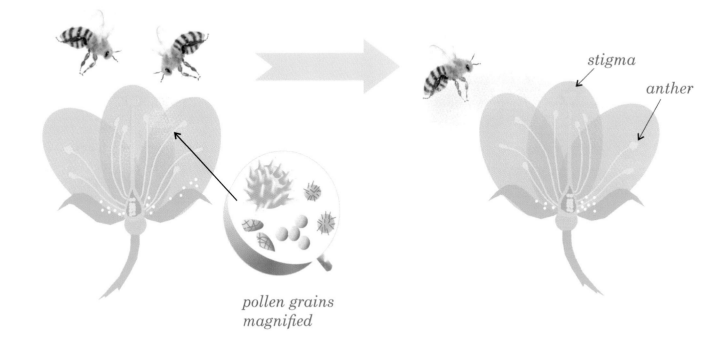

stigma

anther

*pollen grains
magnified*

Pollination is how plants reproduce.

Pollen is the tiny powdery grain in flowers that causes plants
to form seeds.

When pollen is moved from one flower to another, it is transferred
from the anther, the male part of a flower, to the stigma, the female
part.

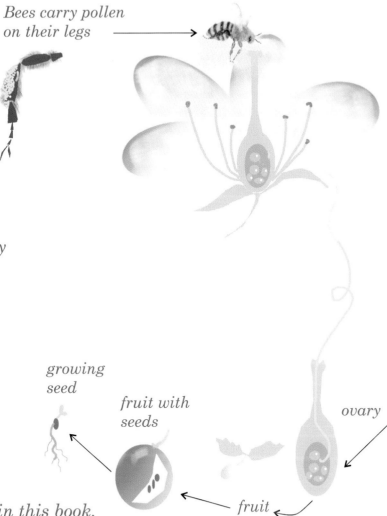

Bees carry pollen
on their legs

Pollen fertilises the
egg cells in the ovary of
a flower.

The egg cells become fruits.
The fruits contain seeds.
When the seeds are planted, they
grow to make new plants.

Plants need help to move
their pollen from one flower to
another. There are many ways
this can happen.

We will show you some of them in this book.
Keep a note at the end of the ones that you see.

growing
seed

fruit with
seeds

ovary

fruit

Some plants are pollinated
by the wind.

This is how most
grasses and some trees
are pollinated.

Because they don't need to attract
insects, wind-pollinated plants have
no scented or colourful flowers.
The pollen they produce is very light,
to be easily blown on the currents
of the wind.

WIND

*The wind can sometimes
fill the air with this pollen
and make you sneeze.*

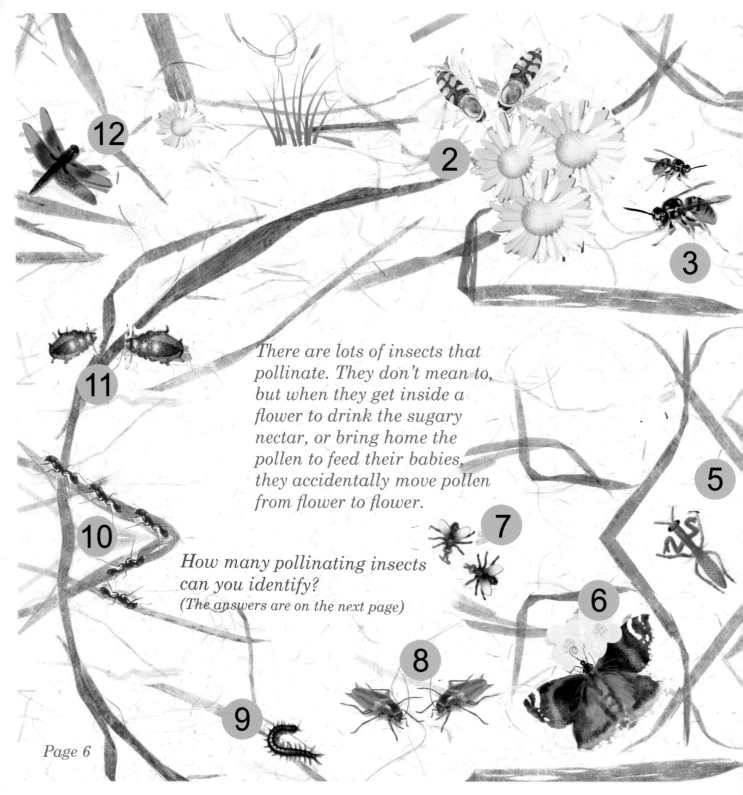

There are lots of insects that pollinate. They don't mean to, but when they get inside a flower to drink the sugary nectar, or bring home the pollen to feed their babies, they accidentally move pollen from flower to flower.

How many pollinating insects can you identify?
(The answers are on the next page)

INSECTS

Flowers have smells and colours to tempt the insects in.

Insects often see different colours to humans.
Honey bees can't see red, but they can see colours off the
other end of the human spectrum. That is why purple
flowers are their favourites.

A flower as we
see it.

The same
flower in
ultraviolet
light, as an
insect might
see it.

Bonus question

Insects have six legs. Which one of
the creepie-crawlies on these pages
is not an insect?

Answers, clockwise from left

1. Bumblebee 2. Hoverfly 3. Wasp 4. Ladybird 5. Cricket 6. Red Admiral butterfly
7. Fly 8. Cockroach 9. Centipede 10. Ant 11. Beetle 12. Mayfly Bonus answer: Centipede

Up in the trees, birds
are good pollinators.

Pollen is sticky, so it
sticks to pollinators.

The blossoms on this
chestnut tree are full
of pollen.

Can you name the birds in this picture?
(The answers are on the next page)

BIRDS

1.

2.

As birds fly from tree to tree, they move the pollen with them.

In pine trees, the pollen is hidden away inside the pine cones, to be released when the cones hit the ground.

Can you name these two common birds?

Answers

Page 8 : Blue tit, Sparrow, Robin, Wren, Turtle dove Page 9 : 1. Blackbird 2. Thrush

At nighttime, bats and moths do the work that birds and other insects do in the daytime.

Bats navigate in the dark and find insects by using echolocation. They emit sound waves and listen for the echo. They use the delay to determine the distance.

BATS and MOTHS

Bats pollinate trees by carrying pollen on their furry bodies.

Moths also have furry bodies that trap pollen, which they then carry from flower to flower. Some moths are attracted by the perfume flowers release, and others by colours that are beyond the human spectrum.

There is a nighttime pollinator hidden in this dot-to-dot. Can you find it?

Clues:
1. It likes to be upside down
2. Join only the white dots

Honey bees transport the pollen in bags on their back legs, and can carry a third of their own body weight.

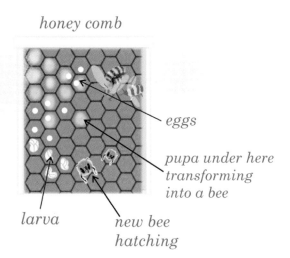

eggs

pupa under here
transforming
into a bee

larva

new bee
hatching

There is one creature that does more pollination that any other: the honey bee. About a third of all pollination is done by this very special insect.

They live in hives that they build from wax.

They move from flower to flower. Some bring back nectar to their hive to turn it into honey. Others bring back pollen to feed the larvae, the baby bees.

As they fly from flower to flower, pollen flies with them.

HONEY BEES

The pollinated flowers can then grow fruits and seeds.

We eat lots of those seeds and fruits. Without honey bees to pollinate the plants, there would be no apples to eat, or strawberries for jam, or oranges for juice, or pumpkins for Halloween.

There would be no nuts.
And there would be no honey.

Some of the foods that come from honey bee pollination are hidden in this word search.
Can you find all twelve?

A	P	A	P	P	L	E	L	E	S
T	E	P	U	M	P	K	I	N	T
S	A	R	O	I	L	S	M	V	R
O	C	I	L	E	U	P	E	C	A
T	H	C	N	E	M	U	R	R	W
L	M	O	R	A	N	G	E	Q	B
P	B	T	O	M	A	T	O	E	E
E	L	D	E	T	H	P	V	W	R
A	L	M	O	N	D	T	H	A	R
R	C	R	A	N	B	E	R	R	Y

How you can help the bees

You can help by:

 Planting seeds that will grow into flowers for the bees.

 Building a bug hotel.

 Leaving some water for the bees to drink.

 Buying local honey.

Make wildflower seed balls

You'll need -

- flour
- soil
- mixing bowl
- water
- native wildflower seeds

Method

1. Mix 10 parts soil to one part flour.
2. Add water until it forms a dough-like consistency.
3. Divide the mixture into golf-ball sized balls.
4. Roll these in the wildflower seeds, then leave to dry for a day or two.
5. Throw them in your garden and watch them grow!

You'll need

- a plastic bottle cut in half, a plant pot or a steel tin
- hollow canes or rolled pieces of paper, 4mm across
- corrugated cardboard
- dried materials, such as leaves, twigs and pinecones.
- scissors
- string

Method

1. Cut your materials so that they are slightly shorter than your bottle / pot / tin.
2. Fit the material tightly into your bottle / pot / tin, so that they won't fall out. Make sure that the hollow ends are facing outwards, and that there is a lip. This will provide rain protection to your bees. You can decorate the exterior of your container, if you wish.
3. Wrap the string around your container, then hang it, almost horizontally, in a warm spot, no higher than one metre above the ground.

Bug hotel

You'll need

- a shallow saucer
- some pebbles
- water

Method

1. Fill your saucer with pebbles.
2. Add water to the saucer - but stop before it completely covers the pebbles.
3. The pebbles will provide a landing station for pollinators, ensuring they can drink without becoming wet.

Drinking station

Keep note of the pollinators you spot, here

_____

_____

_____

_____

_____

Make your bee-friendly notes, here

_____

_____

_____

_____

_____

_____

_____

_____

_____

_____

_____

IRON MAIDEN

A Photographic History

ROSS HALFIN

First Published in Great Britain in 1988 by Zomba Books,
Zomba House, 165-167 High Road, London NW10 2SG
© Zomba Books
Text by Mick Wall
All pics by Ross Halfin
Designed by Jo Mirowski, Mainartery, London
Typesetting by T.P.P. Ltd. London
ISBN 0 946391 65 3

Exclusive distributors:

Book Sales Limited,
8/9 Frith Street,
London W1V 5TZ, UK.

Music Sales Corporation,
225 Park Avenue South,
New York, NY, 10003, USA.

Music Sales Pty Limited,
120 Rothschild Avenue,
Rosebery, NSW 2018, Australia.

To the Music Trade only:

Music Sales Limited,
8/9 Frith Street,
London W1V 5TZ, UK.

ZOMBA BOOKS

The names Ross Halfin and Iron Maiden have been interlocked, both symbolically and professionally, for many years now. Theirs is a relationship that has flourished since the late Seventies, when both were still trying to sniff out their first gigs – Ross to snap them; Maiden to crack them – in a London scene already crowded with better established rock photographers and bands.

They met in 1979, in a pub in Covent Garden around the corner from the offices of **Sounds,** a popular British weekly rockzine Ross had been contributing pictures to for the previous two years. Those were the days when **Sounds** had decided to mount a campaign championing the arrival of a new generation of modern, built-for-the-Eighties heavy metal bands, christening their cause the New Wave of British Heavy Metal. Accompanied by the writer Geoff Barton, the man responsible for coining the shameless NWOBHM tag and who would later coin another – **Kerrang!** – Ross was despatched on behalf of **Sounds** to snap the pix for a forthcoming Iron Maiden feature Geoff was anxious to get down on paper.

It was the band's first major interview with a prestigious national music paper, and Ross Halfin's first encounter with the band that would eventually grow closer to his heart than any other.

Also seated with them in the pub that day was the newly-appointed Maiden manager, Rod Smallwood, an avuncular Yorkshireman who would make the band's big-time dreams and ambitions come true – gathering a mountain of gold and platinum records along the way.

At that time, though, in late '79, the name Iron Maiden was relatively unknown except to a stronghold of fanatical East London supporters that could still be counted in their hundreds. Nevertheless, Maiden's star had already begun to rise. The band had begun to stage their own sell-out shows at illustrious West End venues like the Marquee Club, in Soho. And they had recorded and were about to release their own 'home made' three track EP, 'The Soundhouse Tapes' – a classic one-off debut aimed at, in bass guitarist Steve Harris' words, "the hardest of the hardcore", and these days a much sought after and highly prized item on the collectors market.

Also, though nobody in the pub that afternoon knew it, the band were only weeks away from signing a major worldwide recording contract with EMI Records in London – something Rod Smallwood was even then busy angling for them.

For his part, Ross Halfin's name, though by then a regular fixture on the **Sounds** mast-head, had not yet acquired the stature it enjoys today, eight years and ten times as many tours of America later, If these days Ross is seen as the Quintessential road-worn rock photographer – a veteran of a million and one backstage passes, an airline ticket to some far away location nestled in an inside pocket; a formidable and familiar figure in a thousand dressing rooms, prowling around for pictures with the agitated gait of a prize fighter and a mouth like a promoter's – back in '79 he was still an upstart, a new and quizzical face on the scene who now admits, "I started out knowing nothing whatsoever about photography when I began taking pictures of bands. But I was a fan of Fin Costello's, whose stuff was in all the music papers, and it got me thinking about having a go myself.

"Basically, it seemed like a great way of getting into gigs for free. And besides," he grins wickedly, "I was already big-headed enough by then to **know** I could take better pictures of bands than Fin, or Robert Ellis, who I also used to like a lot."

"Then I went along to a Judas Priest concert in London and took a few rolls of black and white film. I remember expecting sheer genius to hit me in the eye the minute I got my first prints back from the developers. Instead, I took one look at the shots and realised what rubbish they were! Awful! And I knew so little about what I was doing back then I didn't even know where I'd gone wrong. I decided the only way to find out was to do some more...

Then was 1977. Ross Halfin was 19 years old. Having dropped-out of a degree course in Fine Art at Wimbledon School of Art at the end of his first year – "I thought the place was pathetic! A bunch of middle-class snobs who thought gazing at a completely indecipherable Jackson Pollock painting was the be all and end all of everything!" – Ross turned his attention to beleaguring Geoff Barton, in those days the reviews editor on **Sounds**, with regular selections of his earliest work.

"I went to work in my mate's guitar shop in Soho, and at night I used to go out and shoot gigs," says Ross. "The earliest things I did were quite awful, really. But I got friendly with one or two of the other photographers who were also just starting to make a name for themselves in the music business, like George Bodnar. Then Geoff Barton started slipping some of my pictures into **Sounds.** After a few months I started taking pictures for features and interviews as well. Within a year I was practically working for **Sounds** full-time, and starting to travel around a bit for the first time..."

Indeed. By the end of 1978, Ross was dividing his time on **Sounds** between "going around with Garry Bushell and taking pictures of the punk bands he was writing about, and going out with Geoff Barton and doing the same with all these heavy metal bands..."

It was during this period that Ross met up with the now defunct British heavy rock band UFO. At the time, UFO were at the height of their powers; with a remarkable three-man frontline consisting of vocalist Phil Mogg, guitarist Michael Schenker, and bassist Pete Way. They were also, in the late Seventies, one of the most popular heavy metal acts in the world.

Ross had been a UFO fan since his mid-teens (as had, coincidentally, Steve Harris). Meeting them sealed his fate once and for all. Ross' days of photographing punk bands were ended: he would never be known again – professionally, at least – as anything less than A Heavy Metal Photographer!

"UFO were the first band I ever worked with that I really got to know well over a long period of time," he says. "I shot them at this one show, and afterwards we all got on really well together. They probably liked me because I knew all their songs and genuinely liked the music. Then they saw the shots I'd done, liked them too, and a little while after that they took me to America with them for the first time.

"I'd been to America before then, with Geoff Barton on one-off trips to do bands like Styx and Kiss, but I'd never been truly 'on the road' there for weeks at a time, really **going for it**... Well, UFO changed all that!"

The years Ross spent touring the world with UFO – which he did, off and on, until the band's collapse, somewhere out there and still on the road, in 1982 – were to prove formative in his development into the hard-nosed, road-wise rock photographer he is today.

UFO were a band with a hard-won reputation for being the archetypal 'party band', particularly in America, where the band's legendary capacity for unwinding before, sometimes during, and always after a gig, rivalled even that of such acclaimed past masters of the wicked arts of reckless relaxation as the Stones and Led Zeppelin! During the last days of the Seventies, when Ross was first befriended by the band, UFO were as out of their tree, personally, as they were at the top of it, professionally.

Never having witnessed their like before, the young photographer was impressed and decided to stick around for the ride.

"UFO were the ultimate party animals!" Ross laughs, recalling his early days with them, "They never used to pay me anything for taking pictures of them, but they would fly me out to wherever they were in the world, sometimes just for a laugh. And I ended up being on the road all the time, and learning what a life like that was actually like, just taking everything to the limit and trying to keep it together long enough to get the job done...

"It was outrageous really. Everything you've ever read about rock stars going mad on the road, UFO did them all! They'd book the whole pool-side floor of the Sunset Marquis Hotel in Los Angeles for a month at a time, and just have one long party."

The wicked, foul-mouthed sense of humour, so twisted it could take the cap off a bottle; the infamous capacity for excess, recently curbed since his marriage to the lovely Denise, but still likely to wreak havoc on an unsuspecting hotel room if unleashed at the wrong hour; the wind-ups by Trans-Atlantic telephone in the middle of the night; even, I suspect, his worrying passion for Sushi; all are now notorious Ross Halfin vices that began as mere bad habits picked up on the road with UFO.

"They were a great band who just didn't give a fuck about anything they did, really," says Ross in retrospect. "But they didn't know when to stop. It was a shame when they broke up, but you could always see it coming..."

Long before UFO's painful demise, however, Ross had already widened his net, shooting the world's heavy metal elite. By the turn of the Eighties, the name Ross Halfin was synonymous with the biggest and best rock bands in the world. "One of the most important, of course, being Iron Maiden," he points out. The shrewdy.

Going back to that pub in Covent Garden we left the band sitting in, Ross says he remembers that first meeting with Maiden as an uncharacteristically quiet and subdued occasion.

"I don't know if it was because it was their first big interview and photo-session with a music paper, or whether Rod Smallwood had told them all to keep quiet and let him do the talking – sorry, Rod, just joking!" he grins. "But they were all dead quiet and very sort of mild-mannered – with the exception of Rod who is **never** quiet.

"It was a different line-up, of course, in those days (**the Maiden line-up on the day Ross first met the band was: Steve Harris, bass; Dave Murray, guitar; Paul Di'Anno, vocals; Tony Parsons, Guitars; and drummer Doug Samson**), but they were already quite wild on-stage. Out of all the so-called NWOBHM bands Geoff Barton and I covered, Maiden were one of the few that you could tell straight away had a chance of making it big.

"Anyway, we did the session, and Geoff got his interview, which **Sounds** splashed across its front cover the following week. Then we left and I remember thinking, 'Well, they seem like a nice, quiet bunch of blokes. I wonder if I'll be hearing from them again...?' I heard from them again, all right, and a lot bloody sooner than I thought!"

Before the end of 1979, Iron Maiden had announced their worldwide deal with EMI Records, and Ross was promptly ordered back to the Maiden camp to take more pictures of the band – this time in a proper studio, or on location, whatever Ross wanted, with props and backdrops, the works...

"One of the first sessions I did with the band was when I took them down to the London Dungeon," Ross recalls. "And that's when I discovered Rod's 'No Laughing In Pictures' rule! I took this great shot of them all bursting out laughing, but when I showed it to Rod he went (**adopting an exaggerated Yorkshire accent**) 'No, no, nooo! What the bloody 'ell's this?' He absolutely **hated** the shots! It was almost worth it, though, just to see the expression on Rod's face!

"The next time I did a session with them was in Holland. It was the band's first trip to Europe and nobody really knew what they all looked like yet, so for a laugh me and Clive Burr (Maiden's new drummer) swapped places for a couple of shots, thinking no-one over there would ever notice the difference. Then Rod saw the shots and went mad! 'What the bloody 'ell do you think you're fooking doing, Halfin?' He didn't see the funny side at all..."

Despite the occasional palaver over his shots with Maiden's eagle-eyed manager, Rod and the band mostly loved the work Ross had done for them. Moreover, they all enjoyed each other's company: they were all roughly the

same age and had grown up on many of the same bands and albums. And though, initially, Halfin had the edge on 'Harry' and his cohorts in terms of hard road experience, they all shared similar dreams and ambitions.

"Maiden are all really down to earth people," Ross reflects. "And I'm about as down to earth as you can get, so we got on well together from the word go.

"I remember when I first knew Steve Harris I told him to come to a UFO gig and I would take him backstage to meet the band. Steve's hero from day one had always been Pete Way, and not long after I first met Maiden, UFO were doing two nights at the Birmingham Odeon, which I was going to cover, so I asked Steve if he wanted to come along. I didn't have to ask twice! He bought a train ticket the same day, met me on the steps of the Odeon, and I took him inside to meet Pete Way...

"I remember Pete was so impressed with this kid – that he'd come all the way up from London just to meet him, that he had his own band, that he was a nice, genuine bloke – that he let Steve stand at the side of the stage during the show, and afterwards he paid for a hotel room for him, so he could hang out with the band later that night. It was all really nice, and I don't think Steve's ever forgotten it..."

By the end of 1980, a year into their deal with EMI, Iron Maiden had clocked up their first Top 40 single in the UK, with 'Running Free'; their first Top 5 album, with their debut **Iron Maiden,** and had played no less than 137 gigs in nine different European countries – 109 of those in Britain alone! Shadowing them with his lenses, whenever Rod could afford to take him out with the band, was Ross. Cracking a string of disgusting jokes and lewd vulgar asides, Ross set to work capturing so many of the poses, both on stage and off, that this book celebrates.

It set a pattern for Halfin's relationship with Maiden; trapping on film not just the tours, the line-up changes, and the gold and platinum albums, but a whole lot more than mere words could hope to express. Every picture tells a story, they say...Ask Ross.

"I wish I could say I remember the first gig I ever saw Maiden play abroad, but truthfully, I can't. It was in 1980 on their first tour of Europe supporting Kiss, somewhere in Germany. In those days I was absolutely **terrified** of flying, so I always used to get completely pissed before I got on a plane. I just used to keep drinking until I either passed out or was so out of it I didn't care if the plane exploded in mid-air!

"Anyway, Rod had flown me out from London in the afternoon – the idea being I go straight from the airport to the gig, ready for the band to come on-stage, and take some shots... Well, even though I knew I had to work I still couldn't face flying. I had a real thing about about it, which I only lost after I'd flown about 200 times! So, to cut a long story short, I started drinking, and drinking... and drinking.

"By the time I actually got to this gig in Germany, I was so paralytic I could hardly stand up! To this day, I still don't remember a thing about the gig, let alone taking any photographs... but somehow I must have just switched onto automatic pilot, because when I got the shots back from the gig they looked fucking great!"

Those early days on the road with Iron Maiden, when the glamour and the cachet associated with a Maiden World Tour were still years away and when spare money was still a thing all the other bands had, were, Ross says, their most reckless and carefree – young, rootless, with nothing to lose and everything to gain, and just beginning to speed up on the road, Maiden were as hungry as a skinny-arsed street band could be. They were up for it, and Ross liked to join in, then show them the pictures later...

"One of the pictures I took that I remember well from that period," he says, silly grin in place, "is of the singer in those days, Paul Di'Anno. It was towards the end of 1981, on the 'Killers' tour, just before he was asked to leave the band. We were in Europe somewhere, and we were getting a plane for a short hop over to wherever the next gig was. As usual, Paul hadn't had any sleep for about three days and when he arrived at the airport he looked terrible – eyes down to here, hardly able to stagger onto the plane.

"When he got to his seat he passed out straight away, totally unconscious. He had that look you get when the body can't take any more and just has to sleep – he looked dead. Anyway, he happened to be wearing a T-shirt somebody had given him with the name of a new album on it called 'LOOK AT ME NOW'. I couldn't resist it: I took some shots of him collapsed unconscious on this plane, looking like death warmed up, wearing this T-shirt. It said it all, really...

"Mind you, that was a bad day for everybody, looking back. It was one of those days where everything just goes wrong and there's nothing you can do about it. I remember, Adrian Smith had only just joined the band, and we soon found out he was one of the world's most **un**together people for travelling. The same day I took that shot of Di'Anno, just before that, Adrian discovered he'd forgotten to bring his passport with him and the tour manager, Tony Wigens, had to stay behind and help him to find it in time for the next flight out..."

"Later that same night, I'm sitting drinking with Clive Burr in his room. I've just had a dump in his toilet about five minutes before, and suddenly this huge stream of water with turds floating around in it comes floating past our feet! The flush on his toilet was buggered up and when I'd used it the thing just flooded... It was **horrible**! I definitely didn't get the cameras out for that one...

By mid-1982, the errant character of Paul Di'Anno had been replaced in the band by the far steadier, more spirited and vocally much more swash-buckling personality of Bruce Dickinson – formerly the singer with another much-touted NWOBHM outfit, Samson ("Funnily enough, probably the only well-known NWOBHM band I never actually took any pictures of," says Ross, chuckling bad naturedly, "...a fact which Bruce has **never** forgiven me for!").

The resulting **Number Of The Beast** album, single, and bigger-than-ever world tour which followed Bruce's arrival into the ranks of the band, proved to be Maiden's most successful creation yet. In Britain, the first single from the album, 'Run To The Hills', became Maiden's first bonafide Top

10 smash; the album rocketed straight into the Number 1 spot in its first week of release; and, at last, in America the band were poised to enjoy their first legitimate Top 30 entry into the **Billboard** album charts!

The 108-date, 12-country world tour the band then embarked on was their most ambitious and successful so far. By now they were ready to begin headlining at their own arena-sized shows in America; Japan was demanding them back for another sold-out headline tour; and at home in Britain, where they had crammed in 24 shows (including a headline appearance before 40,000 wall-eyed fans at that year's prestigious Reading Festival). Maiden were beginning to assume 'legendary' status in the minds of their vast hardcore following.

"It was some time towards the end of that tour that it first dawned on me how big the band were becoming," says Ross. "Nothing about the characters in the band changed – in fact, that's one of the things I respect most about the band; that they've never changed one bit as people no matter how successful they've become over the years I've known them – but all the circumstances surrounding them started to alter.

"They had a bit of money at last, and suddenly they were famous wherever they went. And then, when Rod said he'd pay for me to fly out to the Bahamas to shoot them while they were making the **Piece Of Mind** album, I thought, 'Hang on, this is a bit of all right! The band must be moving up in the world...'

"The day I arrived in Nassau it was Steve Harris' birthday. I was already drunk when I arrived. I was still nervous about flying, and there was some problem with the plane, which meant there was a six hour delay on my flight. The message came out that they were having huge problems with one of the engines: it kept catching fire... I went straight to the bar and said, 'I'll have a large **anything**!'

"Then, when I finally caught up with the band, they were all in the middle of celebrating 'arry's birthday, and that's when everything went seriously blotto... It was around that time that I realised Maiden had ceased being a kind of new cultish British band and had actually graduated into something much, much bigger."

The final addition to the classic Maiden line-up that was to take the world by storm over the space of their next four albums, was made in 1983, just prior to commencing work on the **Piece Of Mind** album, when ace killing-sticksman Nicko McBrain replaced drummer Clive Burr, who had become disenchanted with the pressures of touring and quit the band at the end of the 'Beast World Tour.'

This was to become the line-up that recorded some of the most swaggering and energised albums of Iron Maiden's career, not to mention their most successful: **Piece Of Mind** (1983), **Powerslave** (1984), the live double, **Live After Death** (1985), **Somewhere In Time** (1986), and... whatever they decide to unveil in 1988 – all have writ the name Iron Maiden large across the consciousness of a generation of mayhem-craving hard rock fanatics, and, as a result, all have sold in their millions.

It was also in 1983, still snapping beach shots of the band in Nassau, that Ross Halfin became Maiden's 'Official Photographer', a job he has enjoyed ever since. As Maiden's official roving eye, Ross has been allowed an unusual amount of access into the private and working lives of the band's members, both past and present, but with particular emphasis on the more interesting, and certainly more famous, current line-up.

Since their pre-signed days of '79, when they still played low on the bill at any number of those infamous NWOBHM nights they used to have at toilets like the (now closed) Music Machine in London, to the five glorious sold-out nights they headlined at the Long Beach Arena in California at the climax of their 11½-month World Slavery Tour in 1985, Ross has followed them every step of the way. At different times his cameras have traced Steve, Bruce, Adrian, Dave and Nicko from their showers in the morning, lens poking through shower curtains like a nose, right onto the stage – up close, hidden behind a side-stage amp, or camouflaged beneath the drum-riser – later that same night. From the dressing room of the Hammersmith Odeon, to the stage at Madison Square Gardens; from the Sushi Bars and Bath Houses of Tokyo, to the grey and undernourished streets of Warsaw; from A to Z and back again – twice! – wherever the sun has risen and set on another Maiden romp, Ross has been there too, one eye squinting into a view-finder, barking orders out of the side of his mouth.

"I regard all the band as pals of mine," says Ross in a rare moment of sentiment. "But the one I'm closest to and probably know the best has to be Steve Harris. Apart from Dave Murray, Steve's the only one in the band who was there from the first time we met up 'til the present day. Dave is so shy, it's only been the last couple of tours that we've even really spoken to each other for longer than about 30 seconds at a time, so it's Steve I probably think of first when I remember all the different times I've had with the band... A real Diamond Geezer and a genuine China Plate!"

I should explain at this juncture about a few of the more obscure Ross Halfin sayings that have, over the years with Maiden, become common-place in any otherwise ordinary conversation with the great man about his work with the band. Some of them, like the aforequoted "Diamond Geezer" and the "Genuine China Plate," rank amongst the highest and most heartfelt compliments one will ever hear Ross Halfin utter. Alongside such redoubtable titles as the Good Bloke, the Bloody Good Bloke, Well In Order, One Of The Finest Men Who Ever Drew Breath, and My Old Doughnut, they are the personalised buzz-words Ross uses to express his admiration or appreciation for the people and places he likes the most. Sincere terms of endearment handed out like laminated passes to the backstage area of Ross' heart.

And you had better become acquainted with them now, because you're going to be seeing a lot of them as you work your way through the splendiferous pages of this book...

"It goes without saying," says Ross, a grin starting to spread across his face like a rash, "that everybody in Maiden is a Bloody Good Bloke, and that as far as I'm concerned they're one of the Most Well In Order bands I've ever had the pleasure of knowing. Damned Good blokes, in fact!

"But a special mention should go out as well to people like Rod Smallwood, and Andy Taylor, the band's managers, who have both proved themselves to be Diamond Geezers and Extremely Bloody Good Blokes over the years; tour manager Tony Wigens, who used to think I was a totally obnoxious waste of space when he first knew me, and who, despite everything, remains to this day One Of The Finest Men Who Ever Drew Breath; to Micky Jenson, the band's American PR, who is a Genuine China Plate and definitely One Of The Finest; and to Terri Berg, who, whether she knows it or not, has always been a Bloody Good Bloke to me!"

Lastly, a word about the title of this book: 'What Are We Doing This For?'

"The demand for new pictures of the band is probably far greater than most people would ever imagine," explains Ross. "Consequently, I'm forever finding myself in one strange place after another with Maiden – Canada, England, America, Poland, Japan, all over the shop! – and having to come up with ideas for new shots of them, stuff that will also give some idea of where they were in the world at the time.

"Obviously, though, most of those shots are taken while the band are on tour, which means we never have enough time for anything; we're never in any one place for very long; and in the never-ending hunt to come up with a shot of them all in, say, New York, but unlike any other shot you've already seen of them, it can become a real battle to organise these things sometimes...

"Anyway, over the years I must have taken thousands of shots of the band in all sorts of different places, places even I can't remember any more, or what we were doing there in the first place. Sometimes it all works brilliantly, and sometimes it

doesn't. Never though, do all the band know exactly why I keep dragging them out of their beds and off to these weird locations. Sometimes the rush for new pictures has been so great even I don't always know where the next batch might be going!

"You can be sure, though, that wherever we go, for whatever new idea I've got in mind, within about five minutes of getting there someone in the band will turn to me with this big pained expression on his face and ask: 'Ross what **are** we doing this for?' It's almost become a sort of standing joke... Perhaps the next time one of them asks me that I'll just throw this book at them!" he laughs.

Well, now you know everything. Or, at least, everything that can safely be put into words. The rest, and there's lots of it, as you'll see, is contained in the unique pictures that now follow.

Right, then. Let's have a look...

Mick Wall. London, 1988.

Extracts from the first-ever
Ross Halfin Iron Maiden
photo-session: October 2, 1979.

MEET THE BAND...

Guitarist
TONY PARSONS.

Vocalist
PAUL DI'ANNO.

Guitarist
DAVE MURRAY.

Bass Player
STEVE HARRIS.

Drummer
DOUG SAMPSON.

The stage-set: Hamburg, 1980.

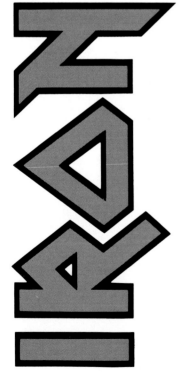

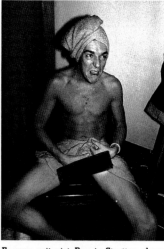

Former guitarist Dennis Stratton shows Ross what he's made of. Circa early 1980.

March 15th, 1980. Paul Di'anno, can-handed, on-stage at the Hammersmith Odeon in London, the night Maiden supported Judas Priest.

October 4, 1980. Backstage before the show in Hamburg, West Germany.

Steve Harris, Dave Murray and Clive Burr proudly display a banner made for them by local fans in Holland on the band's 1980 European support tour with Kiss. "It's a shot that was printed all over the place when it was first taken, but it's still one of my favourites. I think it was the first time anything like that had happened to them outside of Britain."

Dave Murray and Steve Harris, Europe 1980. "More shots that Rod hated," sniggers Ross. I can't imagine why...

Appearing on the notorious Saturday morning 'children's show', Tiswas, 1980.

The Kiss tour of Europe, September 1980.

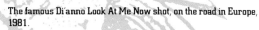

The famous Di'anno Look At Me Now shot, on the road in Europe, 1981.

"This is either Rod Smallwood with an Eddie mask on, or actually Eddie dressed up as Rod, I can't rightly remember. But you can tell it's from the early days, circa 1981, because Eddie's not 12 feet tall yet! A Diamond Geezer, by the way, old Eddie..."

Dave Murray shows Ross the best way to overcome his fear of flying: you crash before the planes gets a chance to do it for you... Europe. 1981.

"Blimey! Clive's just exploded!" Steve Harris on-stage at the Rainbow in London, 1981. A belching Eddie (the 'ead) looks on...

Bruce Dickinson caught somewhere in time... In this instance, 5.00 am outside the band's hotel in Odessa, Texas, August 17, 1982.

Dave Murray on the banks of the blue Danube, April 1982.

A special birthday self-portrait: Ross fleeing the stage in Corpus Christi.

"It was August 11th, 1982, my birthday, and the band were playing a gig in Corpus Christi," says Ross. "Definitely a night to remember, for me. The band dragged me out from the side of the stage at the end of the show and gave me the bumps in front of about 20,000 people! And then they proceeded to give me a bloody good pie-ing! Afterwards, as you can see, they tore all my clothes off and took a few birthday snaps for posterity... It was *well* out of order!"

L-R: Adrian Smith, Dave Murray, Ross, Steve Harris and Clive Burr.

L-R: Bruce Dickinson, Rod Smallwood, Ross Halfin, and Maiden biographer, Garry Bushell.

Another day, another dollar out on the American road: October 18th 1983, on the red-eye shuttle from Tampa, Florida, via Atlanta, en route to Johnson City, Tennessee...

The manager bribes the singer to carry his bags for him... Rod Smallwood and Bruce Dickinson at Le Guardia airport, New York 1983.

The view from the top of the bill; Reading Festival 1983. "The gig that really introduced Bruce Dickinson to the British fans".

Bruce Dickinson and Steve Harris backstage at Reading '83: note the similarity to the sleeve of the Scorpions' 'Black Out' album... Silly forkers.

Dave Murray, Steve Harris and Adrian Smith surrounded by friends, backstage in St. Louis the last night of the American-leg of the band's '83 World Piece Tour.

The arrival of the perpetually combustible Nicko McBrain, seen here enjoying his first tour of Britain with Iron Maiden in May 1983.

Denmark, June 5th 1983. Nicko McBrain's birthday. That's his birthday cake he's wearing...

Dave Murray on his way to work one morning in Denmark, 1983.

Getting in on the act later the same day, Big and Little Nick McBrain! What is it about staying in Jersey that brings out the father in everybody?

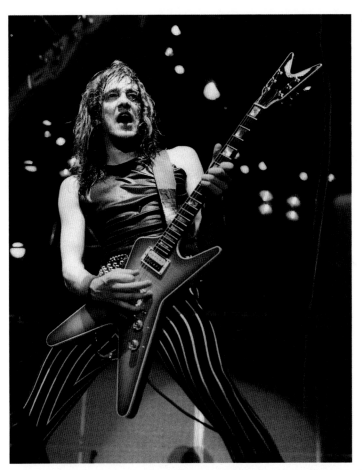

October 8th 1983. The first time Iron Maiden headlined at the famous Madison Square Gardens in New York. "I think a lot of people thought the band were taking a bit of a gamble going for the Gardens at that time," says Ross. "And then they announced the gig, sold 18,000 tickets within a week, and that shut *everybody* up! It was brilliant..."

A pic from Nicko McBrain's first photosession as the new drummer in Iron Maiden, taken by Ross on location in Jersey, January '83. "It was so incredibly windy that day the whole session was a flop, though," says Ross. "Consequently none of the shots were ever used."

Wakey! Wakey! Adrian and Steve taking a break from rehearsals in Jersey, January 1983.

Nico McBrain enjoying life in Jersey after having landed the job as the new drummer in Maiden. January '83.

Nicko with Robin (left) and Donny, who run a club in Nassau called the Waterloo: "Absolutely Damn Fine Blokes running easily the most Well In Order Place to get pissed in on the whole island!" cries Ross, and I wouldn't want to argue with him. Nassau, March '83.

"I call this the Diamond Dave Murray pose," says Ross "The sun, the sun-glasses, the guitar on his knee, the palm tree he's sitting under... and me squatting in front of him aiming the camera at him." Nassau, March '83.

Dave Murray and Maiden producer Martin Birch. Nassau, March 1983.

The mad monk McBrain dressed for his part in the 'Flight Of Icarus' video, March 1983. "Rod absolutely hated this shot," smiles Ross. "He told me he never wanted to see it used anywhere, so of course I *had* to have it in here..."

"I can sing, I can dance, and when I flap my wings I can fly!" Bruce Dickinson A.K.A. The Chimp! flapping his wings in Nassau, march '83.

Ross Halfin earns his airfare out to the Bahamas and back with some of the most tasteful band portraits this writer has ever seen. Nassau, March 1984.

Bruce goes into Total Neanderthal mode, playing in the dirt in Nassau, February 1984.

Steve Harris with the other important maiden in his life, his wife Lorraine. This shot was taken by Ross in Jersey in 1984, during a break in rehearsing new material for the 'Powerslave' album. One for the Harris family album definitely: Lorraine was just a few months away from giving birth to her and Steve's first baby – a beautiful litle girl, as it eventually turned out, called Lauren.

Resident Maiden sleeve-designer and self-confessed mystery-boy, Derek Riggs, on one of the rare occasions he's allowed Ross' cameras anywhere near him: Jersey, 1984.

Live on-stage in Toronto, Canada, November 1984... Eddie's back, he's bad, and he's bandaged! EEK!!

Backstage in Toronto, November '84. "The conditions outside were so rough – about 30 below! – I only took these few shots at the gig," says Ross. "Not that we let that spoil our fun..."

Later that night, live on-stage in Toronto...

Toronto, March 22, 1987. The band are awarded platinum discs for sales of their 'Somewhere In Time' album in Canada.

Steve and Nicko on the tour bus, en route for the Canadian / U.S. border in March '87, helping Ross click away the small hours... back on the way to New York.

The Brooklyn Bridge session

New York, April 1987.

"Ooohhhh! No, no, nooooo!! Not bloody skimmed milk again! Aye didn't get as *big* and *strong* as I am now by drinking bloody skimmed milk!" Honest entrepreneur, Rod Smallwood, taking tea backstage at Madison Square Gardens, 1987.

In the dressing room half an hour before the show at Madison Square Gardens, 1987.

The photographer and the band in action, ably assisted on this occasion by Dave Smithy the band's bus driver and another one who qualifies amongst Ross' hallowed ranks of the Diamond Geezer. Brooklyn, overlooking New York. April '87.

Steve and Lauren Harris.

Rehearsing new material for the 'Somewhere In Time' album, Jersey, February 1986

Dave Murray, backstage, Las Vegas, '87.

Bruce backstage at the Thomas Mack Arena, wondering whether to shave off his beard or not... He still hadn't made up his mind by the time the show was about to begin. So he compromised and shaved off *half* his beard!

Live on-stage at the Thomas Mack Arena, Las Vegas, April 29, 1987.

Bruce before and after shaving off half his beard!

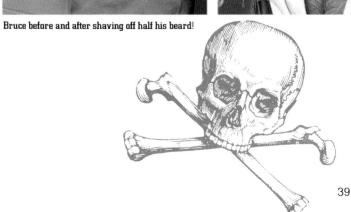

39

In the town square in Gdansk, Poland, September 23, 1986.

Live on-stage in Poland during the band's Eastern Bloc tour, September 1986.

In the dressing room before the show in Gdansk, September '86.

Dave Murray in Roy of the Rovers mode on the soccer field in Gdansk, September '86.

Live on-stage in Katowici, Poland, September 1986.

"The actual gig was held in an old gymnasium," says Ross. "And the show started at some ridiculously early time. If you look at this shot you can see the daylight still coming through the window behind Bruce."

Live on-stage in Katowici, Poland, September 1986.

On-location in the Abbey ruins upon which the Hilton Hotel in Budapest, where the band were staying, is built, September '86.

Live on-stage at the outdoor MTK Stadium in Budapest, Hungary, September 1986.

Backstage after the show at the MTK Stadium in Budapest, September '86.

Nassau '86. "I'd turned up early one morning on one of the days off intending to take
Adrian and Dave out for some shots of the two of them together. It had all been arranged,
they both knew I was coming, but when I got there they were both completely out of their
heads! They'd been up all night drinking together and when I arrived to take them out for
the session they didn't want to know," he laughs. "Adrian couldn't get it together *at all!* But
I got some great pictures of Dave later on because he was so relaxed … so relaxed, in fact,
I had to keep propping him up…"

52

Lining up in front of the old Queen Mary, now moored in Long Beach, California. March 1985.

Backstage before the Long Beach Arena show, March '85.

Steve Harris warming up before the show in Halifax, Novascotia, Canada. December 1984.

Live on-stage at the Long Beach Arena, California, March 1985.

In Japan on the World Slavery Tour, 1985.

Bruce sporting ceremonial Samurai sword, Japan 1985.

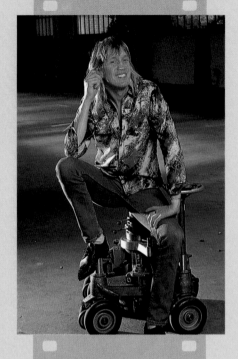

Taking a break from shooting the 'Wasted Years' video in Frankfurt, August 1986.

Note what the boys have scrawled along the top of the beer barrel in the background: *"The Sheriff's Ale. Oh Nooo..."*
This couldn't be an oblique reference to Rod, could it? Naw...

Live
on-stage
Hammersmith Odeon, London
October
8, 9, 10

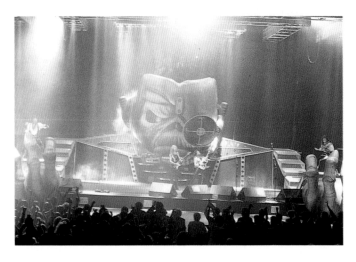

and 12, 1984

Nicko McBrain in action in Calgary, Canada, 1987.

Outside the Hammersmith Odeon, "home from home, init", as Steve Harris puts it. November 1986.

Sunday afternoon, November 9, 1986. Steve and Lorraine Harris host a childrens party backstage at the Hammersmith Odeon, where later that evening Maiden will give a special charity concert in aid of the National Society for Prevention of Cruelty to Children. That's Lauren Harris looking cool in her dad's lap...

Guess who with Jimmy the same night again...? "I was snapping away taking shots of Steve and Jimmy Page together in the dressing room, when Steve grabbed my camera, said 'Get in there!', and I found myself posing away with one of my all time boyhood heroes!" explains a bashful though unrepentant Ross.

Iron Maiden presenting the Regional Organiser for London of the NSPCC with a cheque for over £25,000, the night's takings for their November 9 performance at the Hammersmith Odeon, 1986.

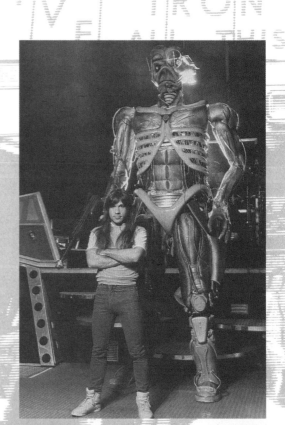

Bruce and his mate Ed. Backstage at the Hammersmith Odeon before the NSPCC show, November '86.

As it was a special occasion, Maiden asked Bad News, the spoof rock band featuring regular Comic Strip faces familiar to TV viewers everywhere like Rik Mayall, Ade Edmondson, Nigel Planer, and Peter Richardson, to open the show for them. Which they did, bringing on surprise guests of their own at the end like Jimmy Page and Brian May. That's Ade Edmondson, alias heavy metal star Vim Feugo, going mental behind Dave Murray during 'Heaven Can Wait'...

"It was the bell that made me deaf!" Nicko McBrain gets his head ringing before the NSPCC Show at the Hammy O. Totally, uh, *gong*-ho... (ouch! sorry about that, just couldn't resist).

Steve Harris and Jimmy Page, backstage at the Hammersmith Odeon, November '86.

Bruce with Jimmy the same night.

November 9, 1986. The Iron Maiden charity concert at at the Hammersmith Odeon in aid of the NSPCC.

... which he did later on that night.

The band presenting a *Jim'll Fix It* contestant with a gold album backstage at the Hammersmith Odeon, November '86. Maiden 'fixed it' for him to appear on-stage with them...

When Titans Clash! Iron Maiden meet Bad News; backstage at the Hammersmith Odeon, November '86. "Not a very pleasant moment for me," Ross grimaces. "I had two cameras around my neck, and I stood there snapping away with both of them for about 10 minutes before I suddenly realised I didn't have any film in either camera! The photographer's nightmare! It was the first time it had ever happended to me... Anyway, Maiden all laughed and thought it was really funny. Not Bad News, though! They were all dead pissed off... no sense of humour at all."

When Titans Clash! Iron Maiden meet Bad News. Hammersmith Odeon, November '86. L-R: (standing) Bruce Dickinson, Den Dennis (Nigel Planer), Nicko McBrain, and Colin Grigson (Rik Mayall). (Sitting) Spider Webb (Peter Richardson), Vim Fuego (Ade Edmondson), Steve Harris, Adrian Smith, and Dave Murray.

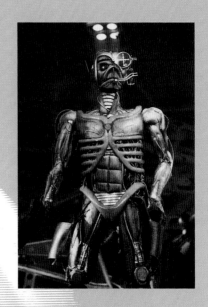

'No, no, nooo! Not like that, like this.... Ooohhhh! Bloody 'ell!'
Rod explains everything to the band about life, the universe,
and the new Maiden video... Sheffield City Hall, October 15,
1986: video shoot for 'Stranger In A Strange Land'

Live on stage in Madrid, Spain. December 1986.

Arise the Great Harrio! 'Arry on the prowl and 'seeking new heights' in Madrid, December '86.

On stage at the Bercy, in Paris, November 29, 1986. "Probably my favourite night of the entire world tour," Ross says. "Honestly, the band were brilliant that night! I mean, I see them play all the time, so I don't exactly go overboard about one of their shows unless I really mean it. But Paris was one of those shows... It was one of the best gigs I think they've ever played."

Another piece of cake... Paris, November '86.

This way
for the tour bus…
Outside the band's
hotel in Dallas,
Texas, March 1987.
"Bruce was upstairs
nursing a cold
when these shots
were taken,"
says Ross.
"He was in his room
shivering
with the airconditioning
full on,
while we were
stood outside in
80 degrees heat,
lapping up the sun…"

Live... Somewhere On Tour in America, February 1987.

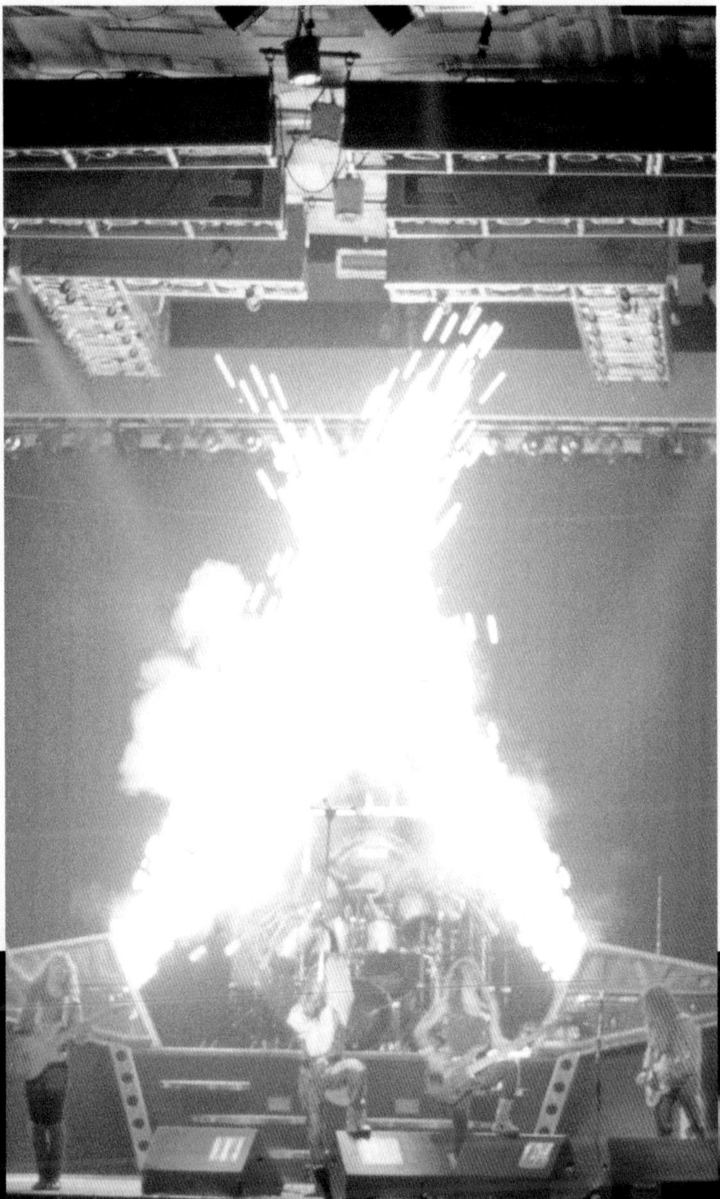

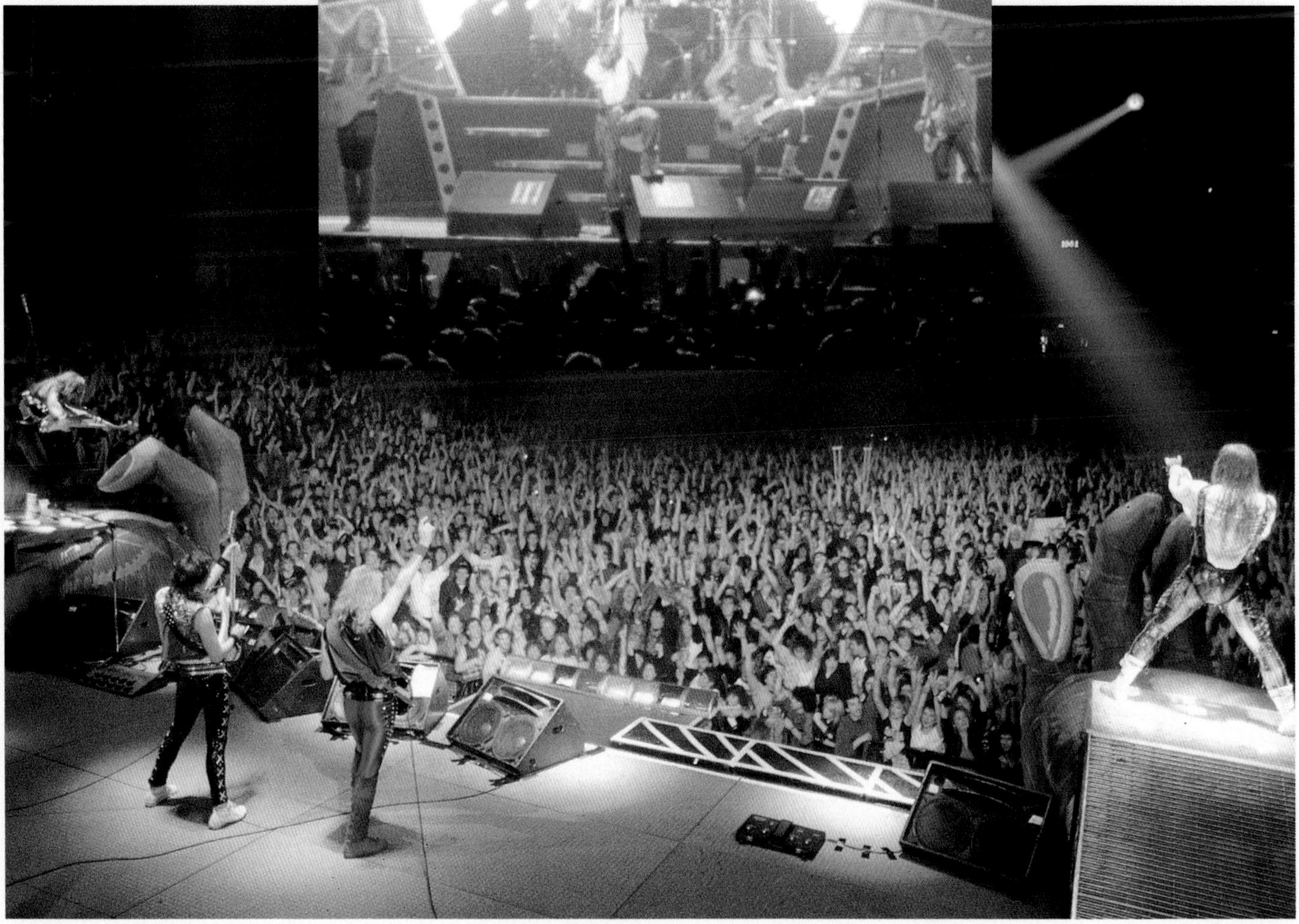

Live... Somewhere On Tour in America, February 1987.

February 27, 1987, El Paso, Texas. Adrian Smith's birthday.

Anthrax invade the stage at Maiden's Meadowlands show in New Jersey for 'Heaven Can Wait', February '87.

Still live... somewhere in Dallas... San Francisco... Long Beach... and back out to Arizona... Spring '87.

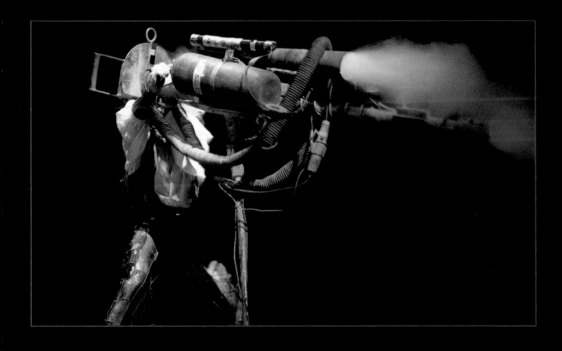

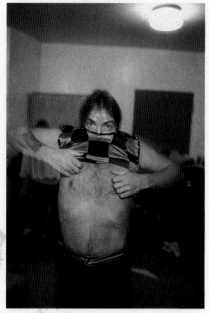

Adrian Smith and Dave Murray in the dressing room before the show at the Long Beach Arena, California, February '87.

Bruce Dickinson being interviewed for American Television, backstage before the show at the Long Beach Arena, February '87.

Eddie hits Sunset Boulevard, threatening to wipe out anyone caught leaving Tower Records without a copy of the new 'Somewhere In Time' album under their arm... February 1987.

Dave Murray asking some Japanese photographers, "What are we doing this for?" backstage at the Long Beach Arena, 1987.

Bill Barclay, one of Maidens backline technicians and Dave Murray backstage at the Long Beach Arena, February '87. Bill was still recovering from impaling his right arm on a fence a couple of days before.

Live on-stage at the Long Beach Arena, California, February 1987.

True to form, the band also commissioned a special birthday cake, which they allowed Rod to attack with a knife after the show. Only this was a cake with a difference: not for Rod just any old mixture of sugar 'n' spice, this one had *gunpowder* added to its recipe! One jab with a knife and... well, see for yourself.

The Long Beach Arena show in '87 also happened to coincide with Rod Smallwood's birthday. This is the special birthday banner Maiden presented their manager with after the show that night. And *no*, of course he's not really 47! ("...he's actually *much* bloody older than that!" – Ross).

The band backstage in Tucson, Arizona, enjoying pre-gig snacks with their head-of-security, Jim Silva. "If you promise not to tell anyone else, I can tell you that Jim is ex-KGB, ex-CIA, ex-MI5 and ex-MI6," says Ross conspiratorially. He also happens to be one of the best on-tour security men in the business. He also likes eating tennis balls.

Vince Neil of Motley Crue (second from left) joins Steve Harris and assembled cohorts on-stage during the everybody-howl-along section of 'Heaven Can Wait'. Long Beach Arena, 1987.

Ross at the set of the 'High Chaparal', now open to tourists, in Tucson, Arizona, February '87. "I took the band up to Squaw Peak to get some shots of them against the sunset," says Ross, "it was supposed to be one of those sunsets you just don't see anywhere else in the world... But when we got there it absolutely *pissed* down with rain! Another good idea down the drain... habloodyha!"

Live on-stage in San Francisco, 1987.

Bruce Dickinson backstage boning-up on a borrowed six-string razor, San Francisco, 1987.

Under heavy fire at the Oakland Coliseum, California, April '87.

Adrian and Steve surrounded by sundry Ratts and WASPS on-stage at Irvine
Meadows for – what else? – 'Heaven Can Wait', May '87.

Adrian caught taking a breather while in the distance Bruce introduces the next number, Irvine Meadows, 1987. Mr.
Non-cha-lance!

Take a bow... Adrian Smith, Nicko McBrain, Lars Ulrich, Steve Harris, and
Bruce Dickinson's bottom... Irvine Meadows, May '87.

Nicko McBrain joined in a skin-beating duet with Metallica drummer, Lars Ulrich. Irvine Meadows, California, May 2, 1987.

Live on-stage at Irvine Meadows, May '87.

The band being presented with a special thank you banner from the local all-rock radio station KNAC 105.5, live on-stage at Irvine Meadows, May '87.

The band and about 500 fans hit a bowling alley in Tokyo during a day off from their Japanese tour, May '87.

Nicko and the band try out a traditional Japanese drum, May '87.

Nicko warming up with some budda-budda-budda backstage at the Budokan, May '87.

Production manager Dickie Bell and Rod Smallwood backstage at the Budokan, May '87.

Dickie Bell, Rod Smallwood, and Nicko at the Budokan, looking to roll...

Nicko and Rod taking it easy before the show at the Budokan, May '87.

Nicko McBrain backstage at the Budokan

The band disappearing out the door of the dressing room 30 seconds before they took to the stage at the Budokan, May '87.

Live on stage at the Budokan, Tokyo, May, '87

STAGE

CREW ROOM

PRODUCTION OFFICE

HOSPITALITY · DRESSING ROOM

Backstage at the crossroads... The Budokan.

"We were all at this temple", says Ross, and the caretaker was dressed in full traditional Japanese gear, so we got him to pose for a couple of shots with the band...

"Then he disappeared for half an hour and came back dressed in Western style, sat next to Steve and promptly put his hand on Steve's knee just to show what a good bloke he really was! 'Arry doesn't look too happy in this one, does he?" Osaka, May '87.

Live on-stage at the Festival Hall. Osaka, May 1987.

Steve Harris involved in his favourite Japanese pastime – taking his daily visit to the local McDonald's. Osaka, May '87.

Japanese tour crew shot, May, '87.

The band showing off some of the special family-sized cans of Japanese beer they had on the rider every night, Osaka, May '87.

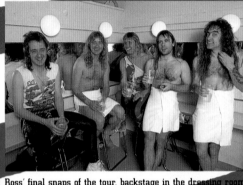

Ross' final snaps of the tour, backstage in the dressing room after the last show in Osaka, May '87.

Steve outside the Festival Hall in Osaka, signing autographs for fans, May, '87.

Well it aint exactly Southend, now is it? Iron Maiden on the streets of old Osaka, by day...

Eddie in Japanese headband.

The band, tour manager Tony Wigens, and assembled personages from the Japanese division of EMI, led by the indomitable Yuri – "a Damn Fine Man!" according to Ross – get ready to swing into end-of-tour-party mode, backstage at the Festival Hall, May '87.

...and by night! May '87.

The Unknown Soldier, is what Ross calls this one. The chap in front of the microphone in the denim and glasses has to be one of the all-time biggest fans of the band. He's never asked anybody for a backstage pass yet, but he still managed to follow Maiden around on their British tours, and then, here, in May '87, he arrived in Japan and turned up at every gig the band played. "He was such an amazing guy," says Ross, "that Steve Harris felt the least he could do was give him a pass to get him into the last few shows in Osaka. Then, the second night, Steve dragged him on-stage with a whole lot of other people that were watching from the side, during the bit where everybody sings along in 'Heaven Can Wait'... But the poor guy was so freaked out he totally *froze!* He could barely move his lips... If you look at this shot you can see Rod bellowing along in his ear, trying to get him to join in."

Steve Harris, Hiroshima, May '87. Behind him stands what's left of the building the first-ever atom bomb hit in 1944...

Steve Harris at Hiroshima, 1987, looking through the Tunnel of Peace. "You look through there and you see the street where the bomb went off..." explains Ross.

Steve and Dave Murray elsewhere on the newly-laid, futuristic streets of Hiroshima, May '87.

Steve Harris and a few of his pals at the peace shrine in Hiroshima, May '87.

者
高

見
言

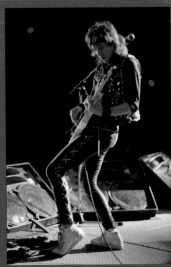

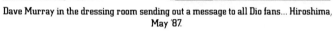
Dave Murray in the dressing room sending out a message to all Dio fans... Hiroshima, May '87.

"Where would I be without them?" (Ross)

Live on-stage in Hiroshima, May '87.

Dave Murray relaxing backstage before the show in Hiroshima, May '87.

George, self-professed 'number one Iron Maiden fan in all Japan', and Steve Harris, backstage at Hiroshima, May 17, 1987.

112

"This was just me and the band bored for a couple of hours somewhere in Japan," says Ross. "Needless to say, Rod hated them, but I still think they're funny..."

Taking the Bullet Train from Nagasaki to Hiroshima, May '87.

The view from the top of Cocovada mountain: Steve Harris and Dave Murray in Rio De Janiro, Brazil, in town with Maiden for their legendary appearance at the first-ever Rock In Rio Festival, January 9, 1985. "These shots were taken on the afternoon after the band had played," says Ross. "They were leaving for New York that night, so me, Steve, and Dave decided to spend the day sightseeing, Rio is such a weird place it was quite an experience... Outside of the few places that the very rich live in, mostly Rio seemed to be made up of third world slums; children begging, thieving and living off the street. Pathetic. And in the middle of it all you've got some of the most breathtaking sights to see anywhere in the world.

"It was a great day, though. I remember we also went to visit Sugar Loaf – which is basically this huge, great rock that juts out of the ocean, and which is only reachable by cable-car. Within about half an hour of arriving, one of the local stall-owners had made all these cups and saucers and plates with pictures of us all posing around on the top of Sugar Loaf! How they managed to do that, God knows. I've still got a plate at home with a picture of me, Davey and Steve."

The portrait of one band and its monster! Eddie and his boys on parade, backstage at the Playhouse in Edinburgh, October 1986.

"I had to fly up to Edinburgh in the afternoon, get these shots done, then fly straight back to London to get them printed up over-night in time for my deadline — we needed a shot for a special Thank You Ad the band were having done for one of the European rock mags.

"Anyway, it was arranged for me to take the 2.00pm shuttle up for a 3.00pm session at the gig. But when I arrived it turned out that 'Arry was in the middle of a football match... He flat-out refused to interrupt his game to have his picture taken, so that was that, I had to wait around for him to finish. The trouble was I didn't have much time; I *had* to be on the 6.30pm shuttle back to London or the pictures wouldn't be ready in time. Finally, the band showed up at five, only straight away Adrian needed a shower after the game, Bruce wanted to finish an article he was reading in a magazine, and I was seriously starting to loose my cool! It was nearly six o'clock before they were ready to line-up for me... I shot two rolls of colour in about five seconds flat, then raced out of the door... Tony Wigens drove me to the airport. Said Tony, *"Self Centred Inconsiderate Bastards!"*

Relaxing in Nassau, during the recording of the 'Somewhere In Time' album. March 1986.

Rod and his boys celebrating his birthday backstage after the show at the Long Beach Arena in California, February 1987.

'Arry chatting up a rather attractive girl fan backstage at a gig... Lauren and Steve Harris in Tucson, Arizona, 1987.

Steve, Bruce and Adrian display the cake the local promoters presented the band with when they toured Yugoslavia. Belgrade, September 1986.

The mean Team... Rod Smallwood and Andy Taylor, taking care of business in Budapest, Hungary, September 1986.

The Steve Harris fancy dress party, held at 'Arry's abode just outside London, July 1987. Guests dressed up to look completely ridiculous included...

Doug Hall (again), Rob Price, Adrian's personal roadie, and um... well, no proper fancy dress party would be complete without the appearance of Wonder Woman, now would it? Well...

L-R: 'Arry, Ross, Rangi, Bill Barclay, Clive Burr, 'Crazy' George Bodnar, and Steve Gadd.

Maiden sound engineer, Doug Hall.

Maiden stalwarts, Vic Vella and Steve Gadd.

Steve Harris with piece of mind Eddie Head which he keeps in the driveway of his house in Essex.

The Photographer's Wedding Picture, Thursday April 30, 1987: the day the deal went down. Ross Halfin finally made an honest woman out of his blushing bride, Denise, and she for her part seems to have almost succeeded in transforming Ross into a normal, relaxed human being! The wedding took place in Las Vegas, the day after Maiden had headlined there at the Thomas Mack Arena, and witnesses to the happy occasion, seen here, are L-R: Pete Way, Bettina, Lars Ulrich, Steve Harris, Neil Zolower, Lorraine and Lauren Harris, Robin Crosby, Crazy George Bodnar, Debbie Hammer, The Groom, Geoff Hammer, The Bride, Rebecca, Nicko McBrain, Pete Mertons, Katrina, Rod Smallwood, Wilf Wright, Malcolm Dome, Dave Murray.

Dave Murray's Hawaiian Wedding, April 2nd 1984.

"This is where the band get their own back on Rod," cackles Ross. "I call these my 'No, no, nooo! Oohh, bloody 'ell!' shots... These are pictures taken of the band in all different parts of the world over the last three years all giving their best impersonation of Rod. Well In Order most of them are too! And then, right in the centre, you see the original in full action... Damn Fine Shots!"

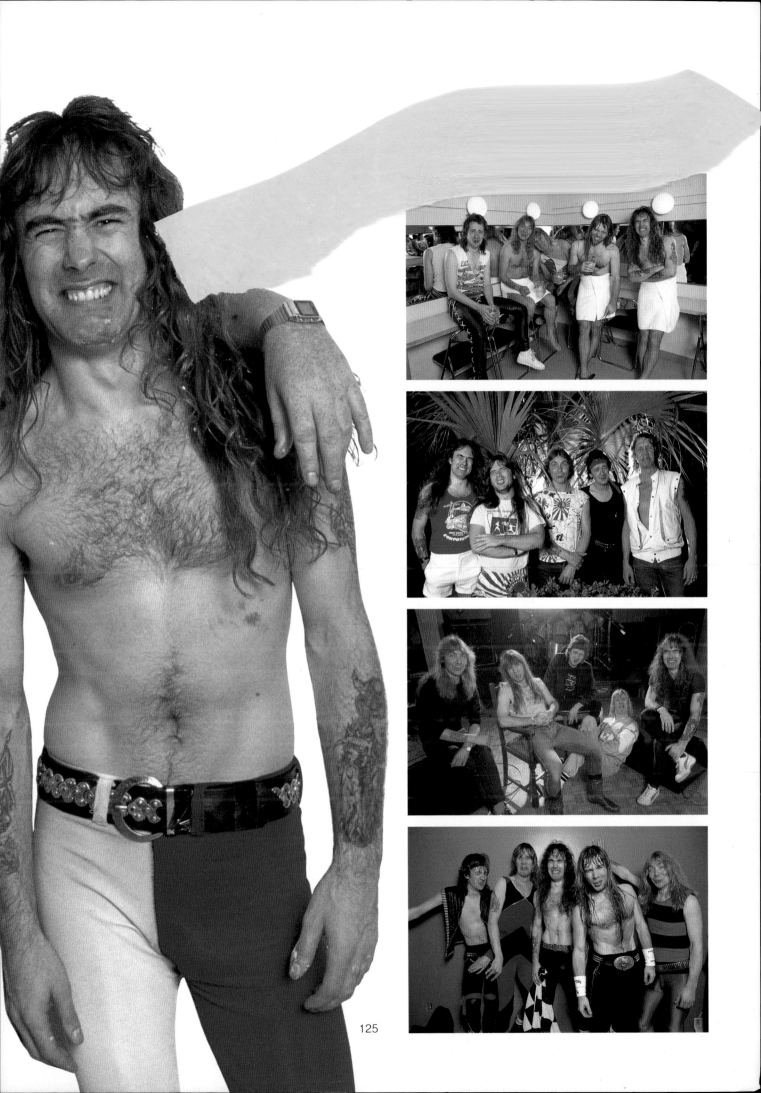

125

Tour manager and certified Diamond Geezer, Tony Wigens, on the observation deck at Ankorage airport after consuming "at least 20 brandies with me!" – according to Ross – and now seen here looking decidedly 'tired' and 'emotional'...

...with Steve Harris.

Ross Halfin
would like to thank George Bodnar
for helping him take the pictures,
Chris Walter and Robert Ellis for selling the pictures.